My Naughty Little S
and
Father Christmas

First published in Great Britain in 1988
by Methuen Children's Books
Magnet paperback edition first published 1989
by Methuen Children's Books
A division of OPG Services Ltd
Michelin House, 81 Fulham Road, London SW3 6RB
Text copyright © 1962 The Dorothy Edwards Trust
Illustrations copyright © 1988 Carolyn Dinan
Printed in Great Britain
by Scotprint Ltd, Musselburgh

ISBN 0-416-13502-1

DOROTHY EDWARDS and CAROLYN DINAN

My Naughty Little Sister
and
Father Christmas

A Magnet Book

This is such a very terrible story about my naughty little sister that I hardly know how to tell it to you. It is all about one Christmas time.

Now, my naughty little sister was very pleased when Christmas began to draw near, because she liked all the excitement of the plum-puddings and the turkeys, and the crackers and the holly, and all the Christmassy-looking shops, but there was one very awful thing about her – she didn't like to think about Father Christmas at all – she said he was a *horrid old man*!

There – I knew you would be shocked at that. But she did. And she said she wouldn't put up her stocking for him.

My mother told my naughty little sister what a good old man Father Christmas was, and how he brought the toys along on Christmas Eve, but my naughty little sister said, "I don't care. And I don't want that nasty old man coming to our house."

Well now, that was bad enough, wasn't it? But the really dreadful thing happened later on.

Dear Father Christmas please bring me

This is the dreadful thing: one day, my school-teacher said that a
Father Christmas Man would be coming to the school to bring
presents for all the children, and my teacher said that the Father
Christmas Man would have toys for all our little brothers and
sisters as well, if they cared to come along for them. She said that
there would be a real Christmas tree with starry lights on it,
and sweeties and cups of tea and biscuits for our mothers.

Wasn't that a nice thought? Well now, when I told my little sister about the Christmas tree, she said, "Oh, nice!"

And when I told her about the sweeties she said, "Very, very nice!" But when I told her about the Father Christmas Man, she said, "Don't want *him*, nasty old man."

Still, my mother said, "You can't go to the Christmas tree without seeing him, so if you don't want to see him all that much, you will have to stay at home."

But my naughty little sister did want to go, very much, so she said, "I will go, and when the horrid Father Christmas Man comes in, I will close my eyes."

So, we all went to the Christmas tree together,
my mother, and I, and my naughty little sister.

When we got to the school, my naughty little sister was very pleased to see all the pretty paperchains that we had made in school hanging all around the classrooms, and when she saw all the little lanterns, and the holly and all the robin-redbreast drawings pinned on the blackboards she smiled and smiled. She was very smily at first.

All the mothers, and the little brothers and sisters who were too young for school, sat down in chairs and desks, and all the big school children acted a play for them.

My little sister was very excited to see all the children dressed up as fairies and robins and elves and Bo-Peeps and things, and she clapped her hands very hard, like all the grown-ups did, to show that she was enjoying herself. And she still smiled.

Then, when some of the teachers came round with bags of sweets, tied up in pretty coloured paper, my little sister smiled even more, and she sang too when all the children sang. She sang, "Away in a manger," because she knew the words very well. When she didn't know the words of some of the singing, she "la-la'd."

After all the singing the teachers put out the lights, and took away a big screen from a corner of the room, and there was the Christmas tree, all lit up with starry lights and shining with silvery stuff, and little shiny coloured balls. There were lots of toys on the tree, and all the children cheered and clapped.

Then the teachers put on the big classroom lights and told us that we could all go and look at the tree. My little sister went too. She looked at the tree, and she looked at the toys, and she saw a specially nice doll with a blue dress on, and she said, "For me."

My mother said, "You must wait and see what you are given."

Then the teachers called out, "Back to your seats, everyone, we have a visitor coming." So all the children went back to their seats, and sat still and waited and listened.

And, as we waited and listened, we heard a tinkle-tinkle bell noise, and then the schoolroom door opened, and in walked . . .

. . . the Father Christmas Man. My naughty little sister had forgotten all about him, so she hadn't time to close her eyes before he walked in. However, when she saw him, my little sister stopped smiling and began to be stubborn.

The Father Christmas Man was very nice. He said he hoped we were having a good time, and we all said, "Yes," except my naughty little sister – she didn't say a thing.

Then he said, "Now, one at a time, children; and I will give each one of you a toy."

So first of all each schoolchild went up for a toy, and my naughty little sister still didn't shut her eyes because she wanted to see who was going to have the specially nice doll in the blue dress. But none of the schoolchildren had it.

Then Father Christmas began to call the little brothers and sisters up for presents, and, as he didn't know their names, he just said, "Come along, sonny," if it were a boy, and "Come along, girlie," if it were a girl. The Father Christmas Man let the little brothers and sisters choose their own toys off the tree.

When my naughty little sister saw
this, she was so worried about the
specially nice doll, that she thought
that she would just go up and
get it.

She said, "I don't like that
horrid old beardy man, but
I do like that nice doll."

So my naughty little sister got up without being asked to, and she went right out to the front where the Father Christmas Man was standing, and she said, "That doll, please," and pointed to the doll she wanted.

The Father Christmas Man laughed and all the teachers laughed, and the other mothers and the schoolchildren, and all the little brothers and sisters. My mother did not laugh because she was so shocked to see my naughty little sister going out without being asked to.

The Father Christmas Man took the specially nice doll off the tree, and he handed it to my naughty little sister and he said, "Well now, I hear you don't like me very much, but won't you just shake hands?" and my naughty little sister said, "No." But she took the doll all the same.

The Father Christmas Man put out his nice old hand for her to shake and be friends, and do you know what that naughty bad girl did? *She bit his hand.* She really and truly did. Can you think of anything more dreadful and terrible?

She bit Father Christmas's good old hand, and then she turned and ran out of the school with all the children staring after her, and her doll held very tight in her arms.

The Father Christmas Man was very nice. He said it wasn't a hard bite, only a frightened one, and he made all the children sing songs together.

When my naughty little sister was brought back by my mother, she said she was very sorry, and the Father Christmas Man said, "That's all right, old lady."

And because he was so smily and nice to her, my funny little sister went right up to him, and gave him a big "sorry" kiss, which pleased him very much.

And she hung her stocking up after all,
and that kind man remembered to fill it for her.

My little sister kept the specially nice doll until she was quite
grown-up. She called it Rosy-Primrose, and although she was
sometimes bad-tempered with it, she really loved it very much
indeed.